THE MEDICAL
AUTOIMMUNE
LIFE CHANGING RESCUE SOLUTION COOKBOOK

HEAL YOUR BODY, REVERSE CHRONIC ILLNESS, THYROID, DIABETES, FATTY LIVER, WEIGHT ISSUES AND INFLAMMATORY SYMPTOMS

CookNation

THE MEDICAL AUTOIMMUNE LIFE CHANGING RESCUE SOLUTION COOKBOOK

HEAL YOUR BODY, REVERSE CHRONIC ILLNESS, THYROID, DIABETES, FATTY LIVER, WEIGHT ISSUES AND INFLAMMATORY SYMPTOMS

ISBN: 978-1-912511-52-5

DISCLAIMER

CONTENTS

AUTOIMMUNE DINNER

AUTOIMMUNE DESSERT

AUTOIMMUNE SNACKS

INTRODUCTION

Your diet plays a huge part in reversing, treating and controlling chronic, inflammatory illness and the Autoimmune Protocol is a fantastic tool for making sense of what you eat, to keep you being the best you can.

Many of us suffer with physical symptoms on a daily basis that we associate with "tiredness" and "stress" and happily go about taking over-the-counter remedies or suffer in silence to deal with them.

Inflammatory processes can start for many months or even years before a firm diagnosis or condition is confirmed and whilst we ignore many of the first signs, there are many things you can do from the start to help slow disease progression and maybe prevent it in the first place.

Your diet plays a huge part of reversing, treating and controlling chronic, inflammatory illness and the Autoimmune Protocol is a fantastic tool for making sense of what you eat, to keep you being the best you can.

The Autoimmune Protocol considers the inflammation in our bodies is caused by a leak of some of the diverse, well developed bacteria we have in our stomachs. This inflammation can start off hardly noticeable as you go about your daily life, but it is possible to be aware of these symptoms early on and to take action.

By managing the types of food you eat, you can improve, prevent and reverse debilitating conditions now and in the future. Working towards building a stronger intestinal lining and removing foods from your diet, known to cause inflammation, is what the Autoimmune Protocol teaches and so many have found this natural lifestyle and diet to be extremely successful.

When the body begins to react to a leaky gut, it starts to attack. However, instead of just targeting foreign invaders, it starts to attack healthy tissue too. This can begin in the thyroid gland, salivary gland and brain tissue to name a few places. Although no one knows exactly what triggers autoimmune disease, it is thought there is an association with different types of bacteria. Conditions, such as multiple sclerosis, asthma, arthritis, allergies, lupus, chronic fatigue syndrome, rheumatic fever and ankylosing spondylitis are just a few of these autoimmune diseases.

Some of the mild symptoms of a leaky gut can be: ulcers, headaches, irregular heartbeat, nasal congestion, poor eye sight, poor memory and brain fog, shortness of breath, earaches, trouble sleeping, fatigue, bloating, indigestion, diarrhoea, weight gain, joint pain and stiffness, anxiety, depression and irritability. All quite vague symptoms really, that many experience just due to lifestyle.

If you are someone that suffers with a number of these mild symptoms, AIP may be of great help to you and possibly prevent future symptoms worsening and becoming really troublesome. Investigating the AIP approach to your lifestyle and diet will be paramount to its success in the long run and there are well trained AIP Coaches out there who can really get you started on a positive step. However, you can implement these changes with a bit of common sense, well researched knowledge and determination yourself.

THE APPROACH ON AN AIP EATING PLAN IS TO:

1. Remove the foods from your diet that are toxic or inflammatory.
2. Build and restore the bacteria in your gut to be healthy, diverse and balanced.
3. Repair the gut. Gelatine, collagen and other supplements and nutrients can help to do this.

INGREDIENTS

There is no denying that only eating foods on the Autoimmune Protocol is a difficult thing to do in the beginning. You will be re-educating yourself with shopping, cooking and preparing and there will be many ingredients you may find yourself missing. However, it is important to see these changes as a minor inconvenience at the beginning of a long-term investment in your health and it **IS** possible to enjoy these foods and embrace these changes.

Removing grains, gluten and legumes is a large group of foods that provide the base and energy for many of our diets, so this needs to be re-established. Reaching for different flour types, energy foods and snacks will be necessary and if you have an unknown sensitivity to any of these ingredients, you may find an instant improvement in your physical self.

Nuts, seeds, lentils, beans and grains are all removed from the AIP diet and these are sometimes the hardest changes to establish. Many of us who follow reasonably healthy diets already, include these types of food in our store cupboards and it can take some effort to eliminate them!

Also removing ingredients that are deemed toxic, such as processed foods, trans fats and sugars can also prove troublesome. Many snacks and drinks we reach for in hunger contain these toxic elements, so introducing homemade snacks and a cupboard and fridge full of AIP friendly foods is key.

So, to look at the core ingredients of the AIP diet, these have been broken down into categories to make it simple and easy to follow. As you become more confident in your choices, you can research more and be increasingly adventurous in your food preparation.

FLOURS

Arrowroot starch/flour, cassava flour, coconut flour and tigernut flour can all be used on an Autoimmune Protocol and although they behave quite differently to gluten flours, baking can be adapted and recipes changed to produce some great results.
Baking powder can be used to help bakes to raise but make you choose a gluten free variety.

FATS

The right fats in your diet only help your health, not hinder it. They can provide support for healthy cell membranes, the nervous system and also enable the body to absorb the fat-soluble vitamins, such as A, D, K and E. They shouldn't be avoided - the right fats should be chosen, and they should always be organic, where possible.

Avocado oil, coconut oil, olive oil, toasted sesame oil, flaxseed oil, lard/dripping, palm oil and grapeseed oil are all allowed on an AIP diet and they all have different uses.

Cooking should be done with olive oil, coconut oil, avocado oil and lard/dripping. Dressings can use the fats that have lower smoking points, such as toasted sesame oil and flaxseed oil.

Baking can be used by a mix of these fats.

VEGETABLES AND FRUIT

Almost all can be eaten in abundance (although fruit in moderation) so it is easier to list the ones you CAN'T eat: All nightshade plants – such as aubergines, tomatoes, peppers, goji berries and potatoes. Avoid green beans, sugar snap peas, peas and edamame beans.

These vegetables are all considered inflammatory.

COCONUT

Coconut products are an AIP saviour. They provide dense nutrition and versatile ingredients and can be used in a variety of ways.

Coconut oil, coconut butter, coconut sugar, coconut aminos, coconut cream, coconut milk, coconut flour and coconut flakes are all available as part of an AIP eating plan and they can create a wealth of textures, flavour and combinations.

CONDIMENTS, SPICES AND FLAVOURS

You may be wish to add some full-on flavour to your AIP cooking and this is possible. However, some of the "usuals" are not permitted, such as peppers, chillis and tomatoes so some creative thinking is needed. The following are all allowed to be added to an AIP diet:

Fish sauce, salt (not pepper), mustard (check ingredients), ginger (fresh root and dried), garlic, fresh herbs, turmeric, vinegar (check yeast hasn't been added), coconut aminos (instead of soy sauce), stock and bone broth.

SNACKS

Dried seaweed, dehydrated vegetables and fruits, meat jerky, fresh fruit, roasted vegetables, tigernuts, flaked coconut, to name a few. We have included some delicious (and sometimes indulgent) ideas and recipes in this cookbook.

SWEETENERS

Sugar is added to so many processed foods and if you were to count up the amount of sugar you consume in a day you would be shocked. This can be through jar sauces, coffees, other drinks, cereals, crisps, dressings and general baked goods. It all adds up!

Sugar is a toxic element to our diets and the AIP diet will encourage you to bake and make your dishes from scratch, knowing what you have put in and allowing you to use the AIP friendly ingredients.

Sweeteners are allowed on an AIP diet, but you must ensure you use these sparingly. They are:

Raw honey (do not give this to under 1's), maple syrup, coconut sugar, molasses (the blackstrap variety has much more nutritional value) and stevia.

PROTEINS

All grass fed and organic where ever possible. Farmers are known to give their livestock unnecessary drugs and medications and the only way to avoid traces of these in your meat, is to avoid mass produced, cheap protein. Beef, turkey, pork (ham and bacon too), lamb, offal, chicken, game, fish and shellfish can all be enjoyed on an AIP eating plan.

Avoid eggs and dairy though, these are considered to cause inflammation. Animal milk, cream and cheese are all off limits.

FERMENTED FOODS

Avoid fermented soy, but you can enjoy kefir, sauerkraut and kimchi freely. No Soy. Tofu is not permitted and is considered an inflammatory food.

COLLAGEN AND GELATINE

These are commonly added to AIP dishes due to their nutritional value and ability to help restore and repair the gut lining. They can thicken up dishes and add binding agents where eggs would have been, and they create some great smoothies.

Gelatine creates a gel like texture that is essential for baking.

Collagen is tasteless and can easily be added to drinks and is availible in supermarkets.

Both gelatine and collagen are great sources of many amino acids that are essential to your wellbeing and a great aid on an AIP eating plan.

When purchasing these products ensure they are natural, AIP friendly, with no added gluten.

AN AUTOIMMUNE PROTOCOL approach to your eating is embracing a new lifestyle. You can take control of unnecessary symptoms, feel energized, healthy and happy. There is a wealth of information on the internet to study if you wish and you can become an oracle of knowledge on the subject. **The Medical Autoimmune Life Changing Rescue Solution Cookbook** aims to igradually introduce beginners to the process and lifestyle and inspire a new way of eating.

Take notice of your body, the foods you eat and give your body the respect it deserves. Exercise a little more and take time to consider the fuel you are giving it. To eliminate inflammation from your body and the damage it is doing, embrace AIP and all the good health it can bring.

ABOUT COOKNATION

CookNation is the leading publisher of innovative and practical recipe books for the modern, health conscious cook. CookNation titles bring together delicious, easy and practical recipes with their unique no-nonsense approach - making cooking for diets and healthy eating fast, simple and fun.

With a range of #1 best-selling titles - from the innovative 'Skinny' calorie-counted series, to the 5:2 Diet Recipes collection - CookNation recipe books prove that 'Diet' can still mean 'Delicious'!

 **CookNation**

AUTOIMMUNE
....
BREAKFAST

COCONUT FLAKES AND ALMOND MILK

AI
cookbook

Ingredients

- 2 tbsp coconut oil
- 1 tsp vanilla extract

- 225g/8oz coconut flakes
- 500ml/2 cups unsweetened almond milk to serve

Method

1 Heat the oil in a frying pan. Add the vanilla extract and stir well.

2 Tip the coconut flakes into the oil and stir for 4-5 minutes.

3 When evenly toasted, remove from the pan and drain on kitchen towel.

4 Allow to cool completely then serve with almond milk.

5 Any unused flakes can be stored in an air tight container.

CHEF'S NOTE
You could serve this flaked breakfast with fresh blueberries, raspberries or strawberries.

WATERMELON, MINT AND AVOCADO

AI
cookbook

Ingredients

- ½ an avocado
- 4 slices of watermelon
- 1 tbsp chopped fresh mint leaves
- 2 tbsp lemon juice
- 1 tsp balsamic vinegar

Method

1 Remove the peel and de-stone the avocado. Slice thinly.

2 Remove the skin from the watermelon and slice.

3 Alternate strips of avocado and watermelon across a plate.

4 Sprinkle over the chopped mint.

5 Mix the lemon juice, zest and balsamic vinegar together and drizzle over the top.

6 Serve immediately.

CHEF'S NOTE
No waste: If you leave the stone in the other half of the avocado and wrap tightly in cling film, you should find it won't discolour and it can be used the next day.

COCONUT AND BANANA PANCAKES

AI
cookbook

Ingredients

- 1 small banana
- 1 tbsp coconut flour
- 1 tbsp desiccated coconut
- ½ tsp ground cinnamon

- 1 tsp coconut oil
- 2 tbsp raspberries
- 1-2 tsp maple syrup

Method

1 Mash the banana with the back of a fork until smooth.

2 Stir in the coconut flour, desiccated coconut and cinnamon to form a thick dough.

3 Heat the oil in a frying pan.

4 Add the dough in heaped tablespoons to the oil and cook on both sides for 1-2 minutes.

5 Serve immediately with the raspberries and the maple syrup drizzled over.

CHEF'S NOTE
Maple syrup is one of sweeteners available to use (in moderation) on an AIP diet, but you could use honey, stevia, molasses or coconut sugar too.

BREAKFAST HASH

AI
cookbook

Ingredients

- 1 tbsp olive oil
- 175g/6oz bacon, chopped
- 1 onion, diced
- 1 small sweet potato, cut in to small dice
- 1 red apple, cored and cut into wedges
- 1 tbsp lemon juice
- 1 tsp chopped fresh sage
- 1 tsp pink Himalayan sea salt

Method

1 Heat the olive oil in a large frying pan. Add the bacon and fry over a high heat until browned.

2 Add the onion and the sweet potato and stir to coat in the bacon and oil. Add a splash of water if it is a little dry.

3 Stir over a medium heat for 10-15 minutes until the potato is just about cooked through and soft.

4 Add the apple wedges and lemon juice and continue to cook until the apple and the potatoes are a little crisp.

5 Add the chopped sage and salt to the pan and stir for a further 1 minute before serving between 2 plates.

CHEF'S NOTE
Use a good quality bacon here to make the most of the AIP friendly protein in this dish.

BREAKFAST CHICKEN BROTH

AI
cookbook

Ingredients

- 300ml/10½floz bone broth
- 3 spring onions, sliced
- 1 handful of shredded cooked chicken
- 1 tbsp flat leaf parsley, chopped
- 4 red radishes, thinly sliced
- Pinch of pink Himalayan Sea Salt

Method

1 Heat the bone broth in a small saucepan.

2 Add the spring onion and shredded chicken. Stir until well mixed and heated through.

3 Add the parsley and radishes and heat through.

4 Add the salt and pour in to a serving bowl.

CHEF'S NOTE
Bone broth contains healing compounds, such as collagen, which is thought to help restore gut lining.

GRAPEFRUIT AND OREGANO GRILL

Ingredients

- 1 large pink grapefruit
- 1 tsp coconut sugar
- 1 tbsp fresh oregano, chopped
- ½ tsp fresh thyme leaves

Method

1 Preheat the grill.

2 Halve the grapefruit and place on a baking tray that will fit under your grill.

3 Mix the coconut sugar and herbs together and sprinkle over the two halves of grapefuit.

4 Grill for 4-5 minutes until the top is a little crisp, but don't allow the herbs to burn.

5 Serve immediately.

CHEF'S NOTE

Grapefruit is a great breakfast fruit if you are trying to remain focused on an AIP eating plan. It can act as a hunger suppressant and may reduce the mid-morning snack attack!

CHERRY AND COCONUT BOWL

AI
cookbook

Ingredients

- 150g/5oz fresh organic cherries, stones removed
- 1 tbsp water
- 1 tbsp coconut flakes
- 100g/3½oz coconut milk yoghurt

Method

1 Make sure all of the stones are removed from the cherries.

2 Add to the bowl of a high-speed blender (reserve a couple for decoration) with the water and process until smooth.

3 Toast the coconut flakes in a non-stick pan. Cool a little.

4 Add the coconut yoghurt into a small bowl.

5 Carefully, run a line of cherry puree across the top of the yoghurt.

6 Chop the reserved cherries. Add the coconut flakes and chopped cherries to the top.

CHEF'S NOTE
Use organic cherries as they have more anti-oxidants benefits.

PINEAPPLE AND TARRAGON OIL

AI
cookbook

Ingredients

- 3 large slices of pineapple
- 1 tbsp olive oil
- 1 tbsp fresh tarragon leaves, chopped

Method

1 Mix the oil and tarragon leaves together and leave at room temperature for an hour if possible.

2 Place the pineapple onto a plate, fanning out the pieces

3 Pour on the tarragon oil and serve immediately.

CHEF'S NOTE
Pineapple contains the enzyme bromelain, which can help reduce inflammation.

TURKEY AND SWEET APPLE MORNING KEBABS

Ingredients

- 400g/14oz turkey mince
- 1 dessert apple, cored and grated
- 1 tsp fresh sage, chopped
- ¼ tsp ground nutmeg

- ½ tsp pink Himalayan sea salt
- 1 tsp olive oil
- ½ romaine lettuce, shredded
- 1 celery stalk, finely sliced

Method

1 Preheat the grill while you mix the turkey mince, apple, sage, nutmeg and salt together.

2 Shape into 6 "sausage shapes" and thread onto 6 metal skewers.

3 Rub the olive oil over a baking sheet that will fit under your grill and place the skewers on top.

4 Place the baking tray under a hot grill and cook for 12-15 minutes, turning half way through.

5 When coloured and cooked through, remove to cool a little.

6 Divide the lettuce and celery between 2 plates.

7 Top the lettuce with 3 kebabs on each plate.

CHEF'S NOTE
Embrace some savoury flavours for breakfast as part of an AIP diet. You won't miss sugary cereals in the end and your body will thank you for it.

CUCUMBER WEDGES WITH AVOCADO CREAM

AI
cookbook

Ingredients

- Handful of baby spinach leaves
- ½ medium cucumber
- ½ avocado
- 1 tbsp coconut yoghurt
- Pinch of pink Himalayan sea salt
- 1 tbsp fresh dill fronds

Method

1 Spread the spinach leaves on a plate.

2 Cut the cucumber lengthways into thick slices and fan out on top of the leaves.

3 Remove the peel and stone from the avocado and mash together with the yoghurt and salt, until smooth and creamy.

4 Mix the dill into the avocado cream, leaving a little to one side.

5 Spoon the cream on top of the cucumber and scatter over the reserved dill fronds.

CHEF'S NOTE
Cucumbers should be eaten with the skin on, to ensure you get the full benefits of the anti-inflammatory properties they contain.

BREAKFAST SALAD

Ingredients

- 1 banana
- ½ iceberg lettuce
- 1 apple, cored and thinly sliced
- 5-6 grapes
- ½ red grapefruit

- 2 tbsp coconut shreds
- 1 tbsp lemon juice
- 1 tbsp lemon zest
- 1 tbsp avocado oil

Method

1 Peel and slice the banana and shred the iceberg lettuce.

2 Halve the grapes and remove the pith and peel from the grapefruit.

3 Mix the avocado oil with the lemon juice and lemon zest.

4 In a large bowl, mix the banana, lettuce, grapes and grapefruit together.

5 Divide the salad between 2 plates and drizzle with the avocado oil and lemon dressing.

CHEF'S NOTE
Grapefruit is a great source of both vitamin A and C, vital for support your immune system.

AIP PORRIDGE POT

AI
cookbook

Ingredients

- 2 tbsp desiccated coconut
- 1 tbsp coconut flour
- 240ml/8floz coconut milk
- 1 tsp ground cinnamon
- 2 tsp collagen powder
- 1 banana

Method

1 Place the desiccated coconut, coconut flour, coconut milk, cinnamon and collagen powder in a small saucepan and gently heat.

2 Simmer for 10-15 minutes until thickened.

3 Peel and mash the banana until quite smooth.

4 Stir the banana into the milk mix and heat through.

5 Serve with an extra sprinkle of cinnamon.

CHEF'S NOTE

Collagen powder is a great asset to an AIP eating plan –it can help heal the lining of the intestinal wall and assist with the issues of a leaky gut.

SMOOTHIE BOWL

Ingredients

- 1 tsp coconut flakes
- 1 tbsp tigernuts, sliced
- 1 tbsp olive oil
- 1 banana
- 150g/5oz blueberries

- 125g/4oz raspberries
- 100ml/3½floz coconut milk
- Extra raspberries and blueberries for decoration

Method

1 Heat the oil in a small pan and add the tigernuts & coconut flakes. Stir for 2-3 minutes until toasted. Leave to cool.

2 Add the banana, blueberries, raspberries and coconut milk to a blender and process until really smooth.

3 Pour the smoothie mix into a bowl.

4 Top with the coconut flakes and tigernuts and extra fruit, to decorate.

5 Enjoy immediately.

CHEF'S NOTE
Make the most of the seasonal fruit available to you to get the best nutrition possible and always try to use organic when following an AIP diet.

TROPICAL SMOOTHIE BOWL

AI
cookbook

Ingredients

- 1 banana
- 150g/5oz any melon
- 125g/4oz fresh pineapple
- 1 tbsp coconut cream
- 1 passion fruit
- 2 tbsp coconut flakes

Method

1 Add the banana, melon, pineapple and coconut cream to a blender and process until smooth.

2 Halve the passion fruit and remove half of the seeds, reserve the other half.

3 Stir the passion fruit seeds through the smoothie and pour into a bowl.

4 Add the coconut flakes to the top and add the reserved passion fruit seeds.

5 Enjoy immediately.

CHEF'S NOTE

Smoothie bowls are so adaptable for those following special diets. You can create some fantastic colours and textures to celebrate all the foods you can eat. Mix them up to get the most diverse vitamins and minerals.

STEWED APPLES AND COCONUT CRUMB

AI
cookbook

Ingredients

- 1 tbsp coconut oil
- 1 tbsp coconut flour
- 1 tbsp desiccated coconut
- ½ tsp honey

- 2 large apples
- 1 tsp ground cinnamon
- ½ tsp ground ginger
- 1 tbsp coconut yoghurt

Method

1 Heat the coconut oil in a saucepan and add the flour and desiccated coconut and honey. Stir for 2-3 minutes until everything is quite toasted, sweet and clumping together. Leave to cool.

2 Core, peel the apples and slice them and add them to a saucepan with a splash of water.

3 Cook over a gentle heat until the apples are softened and breaking down.

4 Stir in the spices.. Remove from the heat and leave to cool in the fridge.

5 When ready to serve, pour into a bowl and top with the coconut yoghurt and coconut crumb.

CHEF'S NOTE
Apples are a great source of fibre and can assist with stomach issues.

BANANA AND BLUEBERRY MUFFINS

AI
cookbook

Ingredients

- 125g/4oz cassava flour
- 2 tbsp coconut flour
- ¼ cup coconut sugar
- 1 tsp ground cinnamon
- 1 tsp baking powder (gluten free)

- 2 bananas, very ripe
- ¼ cup of coconut oil
- 100g/3½oz blueberries
- 1 gelatin egg (1 tbsp gelatine + 4 tbsp water)

Method

1 In a bowl, mix the flours, sugar, cinnamon and baking powder together.

2 Mash the bananas together until really smooth.

3 To make the gelatine egg, slowly pour the 4 tbsp of water over the gelatine in a small saucepan and keep off the heat, to allow to harden a little for 2-3 minutes. Add the saucepan to the heat and then whisk hard for 1-2 minutes until the mixture becomes quite frothy. Add this "egg" to the dry mix.

4 Stir the bananas into the mix and beat until smooth.

5 Stir in the blueberries.

6 Preheat the oven to 375°F/190°C/Gas Mark 5 and line a muffin hole tin with 8 cases. Divide the mixture between the cases.

7 Bake for 15-20 minutes or until golden and a little risen. Remove from the oven and enjoy whilst still warm.

CHEF'S NOTE
"Gelatine eggs" are a good ingredient for binding in AIP baking recipes as they behave in a similar way to real eggs.

AUTOIMMUNE

·················

LUNCH

CRISPY SALMON BROTH

AI
cookbook

Ingredients

- 1 tbsp coconut oil
- 2 small salmon fillets, skin on
- 450ml/15½floz chicken bone broth/stock
- 2 tsp fish sauce
- 1 tbsp lime juice
- 2 tbsp coconut aminos

- 1 tbsp grated fresh ginger root
- 1 garlic clove, crushed
- 3 spring onions, shredded
- 2 heads of pak choi, sliced in half lengthways
- 4 radishes shredded
- 1 tbsp fresh coriander/cilantro, chopped

Method

1 Heat the oil in a frying pan.

2 Add the salmon, skin side down and cook over a high heat for approximately 8 minutes. You want the skin really crisp. Repeat on the other side for 3-4 minutes, until just cooked through.

3 Meanwhile, heat the bone broth or stock in a saucepan.

4 Stir in the fish sauce, lime juice and coconut aminos and bring to a simmer.

5 Grate in the ginger and add the garlic and spring onions.

6 Next, add the pak choi and simmer for 3-4 minutes until softened.

7 Place a salmon fillet, skin side up in a bowl. Pour the broth and half of the vegetables around the fish.

8 Scatter over the radish and coriander/cilantro and serve immediately.

CHEF'S NOTE
Use coconut aminos in place of soy sauce as part of an AIP diet. Made from coconut sap, it's sweet and salty and a good substitute.

CALAMARI AND CUCUMBER SALAD

AI
cookbook

Ingredients

- 2 tbsp coconut flour
- 1 tsp pink Himalayan sea salt
- 1 tbsp fresh parsley, chopped
- 400g/14oz squid rings
- 1 lemon, cut into wedges

- 2 tbsp lemon juice
- 1 tbsp avocado oil
- 1 large cucumber
- Extra olive oil for frying

Method

1 Place the coconut flour, salt and fresh parsley into a freezer/food bag. Add the squid rings and give a good shake.

2 Heat a large frying pan and add 1-2cm of olive oil to the bottom. When really hot, dust the excess flour off the squid and cook in the oil, in batches.

3 Cook for 2-3 minutes on both sides and then drain on a kitchen towel.

4 Meanwhile, cut the cucumber into batons and place on two plates.

5 Mix the avocado oil with the lemon juice and drizzle over the cucumber.

6 Divide the squid between the two plates and serve with wedges of lemon.

CHEF'S NOTE
Squid is known to help the body reduce inflammation and it's also serves up a great hit of protein.

PEACH AND CHICKEN SALAD

Ingredients

- 1 ripe peach
- 1 cooked chicken breast, shredded
- 3 salad onions, chopped
- 1 tbsp fresh oregano leaves, chopped
- 50g/2oz rocket leaves

- 1 celery stalk, sliced thinly
- 1 tsp white wine vinegar
- 1 tbsp olive oil
- 1 tbsp lemon juice
- Pinch of Himalayan sea salt

Method

1 Halve the peach and remove the stone. Slice thinly.

2 Add the peach slices to a bowl and mix with the chicken, salad onions, oregano leaves, rocket and celery slices.

3 Mix the white wine vinegar, olive oil, salt and lemon juice together to make a dressing.

4 Tip the mixed salad onto a plate or into a bowl and drizzle over the dressing.

5 Serve immediately.

CHEF'S NOTE
Peaches are a great source of caffeic acid, which is a powerful anti-oxidant.

CAULIFLOWER AND LEEK SOUP

Ingredients

- 1 small head of cauliflower
- 1 tbsp olive oil
- 1 onion, diced
- 1 leek, diced
- ½ fennel bulb, sliced and chopped finely

- 600ml/1 pint bone broth or chicken stock
- 1 tbsp lemon juice
- 1 tbsp fresh thyme, chopped
- ½ tsp pink Himalayan sea salt

Method

1 Remove the leaves from the cauliflower and cut the florets into small pieces.

2 Heat the olive oil in a saucepan. Add the onion and stir to coat. Cook over a medium heat for 4-5 minutes, to soften.

3 Add the leek and diced fennel and carry on cooking to soften the vegetables.

4 Add the cauliflower, bone broth/stock, lemon, thyme and salt and stir.

5 Bring to a simmer, add a lid to the saucepan and cook for 9-10 minutes over a low heat until the cauliflower has softened.

6 Using a stick blender, partially blend the soup so there are still chunks of vegetables in it.

CHEF'S NOTE

One serving of cauliflower gives you ¾ of your recommended Vitamin C intake, which is crucial for a healthy immune system.

WARM ROASTED VEGETABLE SALAD

Ingredients

- 2 tbsp olive oil
- 1 red onion
- 8 chestnut mushrooms
- ½ fennel bulb
- 2 cloves of garlic
- 4 parsnips, peeled

- 150g/5oz baby spinach leaves
- 1 tsp apple cider vinegar
- Pinch of pink Himalayan Sea Salt
- 1 tbsp olive oil
- 1 tbsp lemon juice

Method

1 Pre-heat the oven to 375°F/190°C/Gas Mark 5

2 Cut the red onion into wedges

3 Halve or quarter the mushrooms (depending on how large they are).

4 Slice the fennel bulb and crush the garlic cloves.

5 Cut the parsnips length ways to make long strips.

6 Mix all of the ingredients together and tip onto a greased baking tray.

7 Tip over the olive oil and massage into all of the ingredients.

8 Place in the oven and roast for 20-25 minutes until everything is cooked and a little charred.

9 Mix the vinegar, salt, extra oil and lemon juice together.

10 Divide the spinach leaves between two plates and divide the vegetables between them too, placing them warm, on top.

11 Drizzle over the dressing and serve immediately.

CHEF'S NOTE

Roasting vegetables as part of an AIP diet is a great idea as it can add different textures and a lovely sweetness that is totally natural.

BROCCOLI & WATERCRESS SOUP WITH BASIL OIL

AI
cookbook

Ingredients

- 2 tbsp olive oil
- 2 tbsp chopped fresh basil leaves
- ¼ pink Himalayan sea salt
- 1 tsp Olive Oil
- 200g/7oz watercress, large stalks removed

- 1 small head of broccoli, cut in to small florets
- 1 onion, diced
- 600ml/1 pint bone broth/chicken/vegetable stock
- 1 tbsp collagen powder

Method

1 Mix the olive oil with the basil leaves and salt. Leave to infuse and for the flavours to develop for up to 24 hours.

2 Heat the oil for the soup in a saucepan and add the onion. Stir over a medium heat for 4-5 minutes to soften.

3 Add the broccoli, watercress, bone broth/stock and collagen and bring to a simmer.

4 Cook for 9-10 minutes or until the broccoli is soft.

5 Using a stick blender or soup blender, process the soup until really smooth.

6 Divide between 2 bowls and drizzle over the basil oil.

CHEF'S NOTE
Basil is a known anti-oxidant and contains enzyme inhibiting oils, which help reduce inflammation in the body.

MUSHROOM, SAGE AND BACON ROLL UPS

Ingredients

- 6 chestnut mushrooms
- 6 thin slices of streaky bacon
- 6 small sage leaves

- 1 apple, sliced
- 1 small handful of watercress leaves (thick stalks removed)

Method

1 Pre-heat the oven to 400°F/200°C/Gas Mark 6 and grease a baking tray.

2 On a board, place all 6 mushrooms.

3 Lay the bacon strips flat down and place sage leaf on each.

4 Place a mushroom on each bacon strip and roll up very tightly.

5 Place all 6 roll ups on the baking tray and bake in the oven for 15-20 minutes until cooked and crisp.

6 Place the watercress and apple on a plate and put the roll ups on top.

CHEF'S NOTE
Sage is known to help with digestive issues, such as cramps and indigestion and acts as a soothing aid to stomach complaints.

SAVOURY CASSAVA BISCUITS WITH SARDINES

AI
cookbook

Ingredients

- 175g/6oz cassava flour
- 2 tsp baking powder (gluten free)
- ¼ tsp pink Himalayan sea salt
- 2 tbsp coconut oil, melted
- 200ml/7floz coconut milk

- 1 tbsp lemon juice
- 1 tbsp fresh oregano leaves, chopped
- 2x 90g tins of sardines in olive oil
- 1 handful of rocket leaves
- Wedges of lemon

Method

1 Pre-heat the oven to 400°F/200°C/Gas Mark 6.

2 To make the biscuits, mix the flour, baking powder, salt, coconut oil, coconut milk and oregano together. Adjust the qauntity of milk, if need be, to create a firm dough.

3 Roll out the dough to about 2cm deep and cut 9 cookie shapes out.

4 Place on a greased baking tray and bake in the oven for 15-20 minutes, or until risen and cooked.

5 Slice 2 of the biscuits in half (keep the others stored for another time) and place cut side up, on a tray that will go under the grill.

6 Mash the sardines from the tin and spread on top of the biscuits.

7 Place the tray under a hot grill and toast until the sardines are crisped and heated through.

8 Put 2 halves on one plate each and top with some rocket leaves and a lemon wedge.

CHEF'S NOTE

Tinned sardines are an AIP store cupboard essential. Full of omega-3 and calcium, but make sure you only get the ones packed in olive oil and not tomato sauce!

STIR FRY SALAD

Ingredients

- 1 tbsp olive oil
- 6 brussel sprouts, shredded
- 2 leaves of Chinese lettuce, shredded
- 3 chestnut mushrooms, sliced
- 1 red onion, halved and sliced
- 1 garlic clove, crushed
- 1 tsp fresh grated ginger root

For The Dressing
- ½ tbsp coconut aminos
- 1 tbsp lime juice
- 1 tbsp olive oil
- ½ tsp pink Himalayan sea salt

Method

1 Heat the olive oil in a large frying pan or wok.

2 Add the Brussel sprouts, Chinese lettuce, mushrooms, red onion, garlic and ginger.

3 Stir fry for 9-10 minutes until the vegetables are soft but still with a little crunch.

4 Place everything into a bowl or on a plate.

5 Mix together all of the dressing ingredients and drizzle over the salad.

CHEF'S NOTE
Brussel sprouts are part of the cruciferous vegetable family, all of which are known for their anti-oxidant and anti-inflammatory properties.

GRILLED ASPARAGUS WITH LEMON CREAM

AI
cookbook

Ingredients

- 1 tbsp olive oil
- ¼ tsp Himalayan sea salt
- 1 tsp fresh dill, shredded
- 6 spears of asparagus

- ½ avocado
- 1 tbsp coconut yoghurt
- 1 lemon, zest only
- 1 tbsp fresh dill fronds extra to serve

Method

1 Pre-heat the grill.

2 Mix the olive oil with the salt and dill.

3 Remove any thick fibrous parts from the asparagus spears.

4 Brush the oil over the asparagus and place under a hot grill and cook for 6-7 minutes, turning half way through.

5 Peel and de-stone from the avocado. Scoop out the flesh and mash with a fork until really smooth.

6 Mix the coconut yoghurt into the avocado and add the lemon zest.

7 Place the grilled asparagus on to a plate and top with the avocado and lemon cream.

8 Decorate with a little extra fresh dill.

CHEF'S NOTE
You could use either the green or purple variety of asparagus for this dish but try to avoid the white one; they are grown in the dark and don't have the same rich beneficial phytochemicals.

SUMMER HERB BOWL AND MUSTARD DRIZZLE

AI cookbook

Ingredients

- 150g/5oz rocket leaves
- 75g/3oz baby spinach leaves
- 1 small bunch of flat leaf parsley
- 1 small bunch of chives
- 1 tbsp fresh oregano leaves, chopped
- 1 tbsp fresh mint leaves, chopped

- Small handful of wild garlic (optional, if it's available)
- 1 tbsp avocado oil
- 1 tsp organic Dijon mustard
- 1 tsp maple syrup
- 2 tbsp apple cider vinegar

Method

1 Place the rocket leaves and spinach leaves onto a plate.

2 Chop the parsley and chives and mix up with the leaves on the plate.

3 Sprinkle over the oregano and mint and the wild garlic, if using.

4 Mix the avocado oil with the mustard, maple syrup and vinegar.

5 Drizzle over 1-2 tbsps of the mustard drizzle, leaving any excess for another day.

CHEF'S NOTE
Make sure you use the apple cider vinegar variety that has no added yeast, as this should be avoided on an AIP diet.

STRAWBERRY FIELDS

AI
cookbook

Ingredients

- 5 strawberries, hulled and sliced
- 1 tbsp fresh mint leaves
- ½ medium cucumber
- ½ avocado
- 175g/6oz baby spinach leaves

- 75g/3oz rocket leaves
- 1 tbsp olive oil
- 1 tbsp balsamic vinegar
- ½ lemon juice
- Pinch of Himalayan sea salt

Method

1 Place the strawberries and mint into a bowl.

2 Halve and slice the cucumber, leaving the skin and seeds intact.

3 Peel and remove the stone from the avocado and slice the flesh.

4 Mix the olive oil, balsamic, lemon juice and salt together.

5 Add the cucumber, avocado and salad leaves to the strawberries and toss together.

6 Tip onto a plate and drizzle over the dressing.

CHEF'S NOTE

It is better to make your own dressings for salads as most shop brought varieties have added black pepper, which needs to be avoided on an AIP eating plan.

SUNDAY VEG BOWL

AI
cookbook

Ingredients

- 1 tsp olive oil
- 3 cavolo nero leaves, shredded
- 3 green cabbage leaves, shredded
- Handful of kale, shredded, tough stalks removed
- ½ a leek, chopped
- 1 garlic clove, crushed

For The Drizzle
- 1 tbsp olive oil
- 1 tsp onion powder
- ½ tbsp balsamic vinegar
- ½ tbsp coconut aminos

Method

1 Heat the oil in a frying pan or wok.

2 Add the cavolo nero, cabbage, kale, leek and garlic and stir fry for 5-6 minutes, until the greens have wilted.

3 Stir the drizzle ingredients into the pan and cook for a further 1-2 minutes to heat through.

4 Serve immediately.

CHEF'S NOTE
Cavolo nero is one of the darkest green brassica vegetables and a rich source of beta-carotenes.

SPICED CHICKEN FLATBREAD

AI cookbook

Ingredients

For The Flatbread
- 125g/4oz tapioca starch
- 4 tbsp coconut flour
- 1 tsp onion powder
- 1 tsp cream of tartar
- ½ tsp baking powder

- 2 tbsp olive oil
- 120-150ml/4-5floz of warm water

For The Chicken
- 1 onion, halved and sliced
- 1 large handful of cooked chicken breast, shredded

- 1 tsp olive oil
- 1 tsp ground ginger
- ½ tsp ground cinnamon
- ½ tsp turmeric
- Handful of rocket leaves

Method

1 Pre-heat the oven to 400°F/200°C/Gas Mark 6 and line a baking tray.

2 Mix the tapioca starch with the coconut flour, onion powder, cream of tartar and baking powder.

3 Pour in the olive oil and enough warm water to make a crumbly dough.

4 Press on a to the baking tray and roll flat to create a circle.

5 Bake in the oven for 10-15 minutes until cooked.

6 Meanwhile, heat the oil in a saucepan and add the sliced onion. Stir and cook over a low heat for 10 minutes, until caramelised and sweet.

7 Stir in the chicken and spices and cook for a further 2 minutes to heat through.

8 Put the rocket on top of the flatbread and top with the chicken mix.

CHEF'S NOTE
Arrowroot may be used in replacement of the tapioca starch if you prefer.

SPICED RAW CAULIFLOWER

Ingredients

- 200g/7oz cauliflower, chopped into mini florets
- 2 tbsp flat leaf parsley, chopped
- 2 tbsp fresh oregano, chopped
- 1 tbsp fresh coriander/cilantro, chopped
- 1 tbsp pomegranate seeds

- 2 tbsp coconut oil, melted
- ½ tsp ground ginger
- ½ tsp ground cinnamon
- ½ tsp turmeric
- Pinch of Himalayan sea salt

Method

1 Mix the cauliflower, parsley, oregano, coriander/cilantro and pomegranate seeds together.

2 Mix the coconut oil, spices and salt together and pour over the cauliflower.

3 Leave to soak for an hour if possible before serving, to allow the flavours to develop and penetrate the cauliflower.

CHEF'S NOTE
Pomegranates are full of vitamin C and a great addition to an AIP diet as they add some welcome texture and crunch to a dish.

TUNA AND RED ONION PACKED LUNCH

AI
cookbook

Ingredients

- 125g/4oz tin of tinned tuna
- 1 small red onion, halved and sliced
- 1 tsp olive oil
- 1 tbsp lemon zest
- Pinch of Himalayan sea salt

- ½ avocado
- ¼ iceburg lettuce, shredded
- 1 red apple
- 1 tbsp lemon juice

Method

1 Drain the tuna and flake evenly. Stir through the onions, olive oil, lemon zest and salt.

2 Place at one end of a plastic lunch box.

3 Peel and remove the stone from the avocado and slice. Place in a line next to the tuna.

4 Add the shredded lettuce to the container next to the avocado.

5 Wash, core and slice the apple. Mix with the lemon juice to prevent it from browning.

6 Place the apple next to the lettuce.

7 Put the lid on and pack a fork.

CHEF'S NOTE
Tinned tuna is a tasty protein to add to an AIP meal, but try and make sure you purchase the "line caught" tuna.

AUTOIMMUNE

· · · · · · · · · · · · · · · · · ·

DINNER

PORK GRILLED & PINEAPPLE AND BOWL

Ingredients

- ½ small pineapple, cut into wedges
- 1 tbsp olive oil
- 1 tsp raw honey
- 1 pork loin steak
- 1 handful of rocket leaves
- 1 celery stalk, sliced

- ¼ cucumber
- 1 tbsp avocado oil
- 1 tbsp lemon juice
- 1 tbsp flat leaf parsley, chopped
- ¼ tsp pink Himalayan sea salt

Method

1 Heat a griddle pan until scorching hot.

2 Mix the olive oil and honey together and brush over both sides of the pork.

3 Griddle the pork on both sides for 7-8 minutes, until charred, caramelized and cooked.

4 Add the pineapple to the pan and cook for 1-2 minutes on both sides.

5 Place the rocket, celery and cucumber in a bowl.

6 Slice the pork and put into the bowl with the salad, parsley and pineapple.

7 Mix the salt, avocado oil and lemon juice together and drizzle over the top.

8 Serve immediately.

CHEF'S NOTE
Avocado oil is a great base for an AIP salad dressing as it has a mild sweet and nutty flavour and also provides protective carotenoids.

TUNA AND CARAMELISED ONION PIZZA

AI cookbook

Ingredients

For The Pizza Base
- 85g/3oz arrowroot starch
- 4 tbsp coconut flour
- 1 tsp cream of tartar
- ½ tsp baking powder
- ½ tsp pink Himalayan sea salt
- 2 tbsp olive oil

- 120ml/4floz warm water

For The Topping
- 1 tbsp olive oil
- 2 red onion, halved and sliced
- 200g/7oz tin of tuna
- 7-8 black olives, chopped
- 150g/5oz rocket leaves

- Small bunch of flat leaf parsley
- Small bunch of fresh oregano
- 4-5 fresh basil leaves
- 3 tbsp olive oil
- 2 tbsp lemon juice

Method

1 Mix the pizza base ingredients together until a firm dough is formed.

2 Press down onto the baking tray, forming a circle.

3 Bake in the oven for 15-20 minutes, until golden and cooked.

4 In a frying pan, add the onions and oil and heat over a medium heat for 8-10 minutes. Stir until softened and sweet.

5 Add the tuna and olives to the pan and stir until the tuna is broken up and everything is well combined.

6 Place the herbs oil and lemon juice into a blender and process until smooth.

7 To serve, place the pizza base on a board, scatter over the rocket leaves. Add the tuna mix and drizzle over the herb oil.

8 Cut in to 4 wedges.

CHEF'S NOTE
Olives contain vitamin E and lots of iron and also add a tasty, salty flavour to a dish without having to add any extra seasoning.

PORK, SWEET POTATO AND APPLE BAKE

AI
cookbook

Ingredients

- 1 small sweet potato
- 1 boneless pork chop
- 4 sage leaves, roughly chopped
- 1 red skinned apple, cored and sliced
- ½ tsp pink Himalayan sea salt
- 1 tbsp olive oil
- 4-5 florets of broccoli

Method

1 Pre-heat the oven to 375°F/190°C/Gas Mark 5 and grease a small casserole dish.

2 Cut the sweet potato in to wedges and put into the casserole dish.

3 Scatter over the apple pieces and sage leaves and season with the salt.

4 Place the pork chop on top and drizzle the olive oil over.

5 Bake in the oven for 20-25 minutes until the potato is soft and the pork cooked through.

6 Steam or boil the broccoli and serve immediately.

CHEF'S NOTE
Pork contains useful levels of zinc, which supports healthy immune functions.

PORK CHOPS WITH MANGO RELISH

AI
cookbook

Ingredients

- 2 pork chops
- Zest and juice of 1 orange
- 1 tbsp rosemary leaves
- 1 tbsp coconut aminos
- 1 tbsp coconut oil, melted
For The Mango Relish
- ½ cucumber, finely diced

- 1 red onion, halved and finely diced
- 1 mango, peeled and stone removed, and finely diced
- Medium bunch of coriander/cilantro, chopped
- 1 tbsp olive oil

- ½ avocado, peeled, de-stoned and finely diced
- ¼ tsp pink Himalayan sea salt
- 4-5 sliced radishes to serve

Method

1 Mix the pork chops with the orange zest, juice, rosemary leaves, coconut aminos and coconut oil. Leave to marinade in a non-metallic bowl for 24 ours if possible.

2 When ready to serve, heat grill to a medium heat and place the pork under. Cook for 9-10 minutes on both sides, until cooked through.

3 Meanwhile, mix all of the other ingredients together for the mango relish.

4 Put one pork chop on a plate and spoon over half of the relish.

5 Top with the sliced radishes and repeat with the other plate.

CHEF'S NOTE
Mangoes contain stomach soothing enzymes and have been used as an ingredient to treat digestive issues for centuries.

MEATBALLS AND COURGETTI

AI
cookbook

Ingredients

- 2 tbsp olive oil
- 1 white onion, finely diced
- 3 garlic cloves, crushed
- ¼ tsp pink Himalayan sea salt
- 1 tbsp dried oregano
- 300g/11oz beef mince

- ½ fennel bulb, shredded
- 1 tbsp gelatine +4 tbsp hot water
- 1 red onion, halved and sliced
- 8 chestnut mushrooms, sliced
- 300g/11oz courgette noodles (courgettes/zucchini spiralized)

Method

1 Heat the 1 tbsp oil for the meatballs in a frying pan and add the white onion and 1 garlic clove. Cook for 4-5 minutes until softened. Leave to cool a little.

2 In a bowl, add the oregano, salt and minced beef.

3 Mix the gelatine with the hot water and whisk hard for 1-2 minutes until frothy.

4 Mix the mince, gelatine and cooled onions and garlic. With damp hands, roll in to 10 balls.

5 In the same frying pan, add the rest of the oil and gently heat. Add the red onion, fennel and 2 garlic cloves and cook until softened.

6 Add the mushrooms and cook over a high heat to release the juices.

7 Add the meatballs to the pan and cook over a high heat to brown.

8 Cook for 15-20 minutes over a medium heat, until the meatballs are cooked through.

9 Add the courgette to the pan and stir for 2-3 minutes to coat in the oils and soften a little.

10 Divide between 2 plates and serve immediately.

CHEF'S NOTE
Vegetables that have been spiralized are a great aid for an AIP eating plan. They can replace pasta and noodles quite easily and they're full of plant nutrition.

52

PRAWN AND ASPARAGUS "RISOTTO"

AI
cookbook

Ingredients

- 1 tsp olive oil
- 1 onion, diced
- 1 garlic clove, crushed
- 1 large cauliflower
- 5-6 spears of asparagus, chopped

- ¼ pink Himalayan sea salt
- 200g/7oz cooked prawns
- 1 lemon, juice and zest
- 150g/5oz watercress, thick stalks removed

Method

1 Heat the oil in a large frying pan or wok. Add the onion and garlic and cook over a medium heat for 4-5 minutes until softened.

2 Process the cauliflower in a blender until it resembles rice grains.

3 Add the cauliflower and the asparagus to the pan and stir fry for 4-5 minutes until softened, but still with a little bite.

4 Add the salt, prawns, lemon juice and zest and cook until the prawns are heated through.

5 Divide between 2 plates and top with the watercress.

CHEF'S NOTE

Prawns are a quick dinner time ingredient that are full of protein and B vitamins, crucial for metabolism and cell function.

BAKED POTATOES WITH CHICKEN LIVER

AI cookbook

Ingredients

- 2 medium sweet potatoes, baked
- 1 tbsp olive oil
- 1 carrot, chopped finely
- 1 celery stalk, chopped finely
- 1 onion, chopped finely
- 1 garlic clove

- 300g/11oz chicken livers
- 300ml beef bone broth
- 1 tbsp coconut aminos
- 1 bay leaf
- 1 tbsp rosemary leaves, chopped
- 200g/7oz spinach leaves, steamed

Method

1 Heat the oil in a frying pan and add the carrot, celery, onion and garlic and cook over a medium heat for 5-6 minutes, until softened.

2 Turn the heat up and add the chicken livers. Cook for 10 minutes until browned.

3 Pour over the bone broth, coconut aminos, bay leaf and rosemary leaves.

4 Simmer for 10 minutes until thickened a little and livers cooked.

5 Serve immediately, spooned on top of the sweet potatoes with some steamed spinach.

CHEF'S NOTE

When following an AIP eating plan, it is really worthwhile trying to eat one serving of organ meat once a week. Chicken livers are full of flavour and very cheap!

COD LAKSA

AI
cookbook

Ingredients

- 1 onion, finely diced
- 1 tbsp grated fresh ginger root
- 1 stalk of lemongrass, chopped roughly
- 1 tbsp coconut oil
- 1 tsp turmeric
- 1 garlic clove, crushed
- 600ml/1 pint coconut milk

- 450ml/15½floz chicken stock
- 2 pak choi, leaves sliced lengthways
- 200g/7oz courgette noodles
- 2 large cod fillets
- 1 tbsp shredded lime zest and 2 tbsp chopped fresh coriander/cilantro to serve
- 3 spring onions, shredded

Method

1 To make the laksa base, put the onion, ginger and lemongrass into a blender and process until smooth.

2 Add the coconut oil to a saucepan and add the garlic. Cook briefly over a gentle heat.

3 Add the onion base and cook for 4-5 minutes to soften and allow the flavours to release.

4 Add the coconut milk, stock and turmeric and simmer gently for 10 minutes, adding the pak choi and courgette noodles towards the end.

5 Pour water in to a deep pan and poach the cod for 7-8 minutes until cooked and just flaking.

6 Put the fillets into 2 bowls.

7 Tip over the coconut laksa liquid, ensuring the vegetables are equal.

8 Top with the spring onion, shredded lime zest and fresh coriander/cilantro.

CHEF'S NOTE

The diuretic effect of lemongrass assists the kidneys in removing toxins, by increased urination, working as a great anti-oxidant.

ROAST CHICKEN WITH SALSA VERDE

Ingredients

- 1 tbsp olive oil
- 4 chicken thighs
- 8 garlic cloves
- 1 lemon, cut in to wedges
- 1 tsp pink Himalayan sea salt

For The Salsa Verde
- 1 large bunch of flat leaf parsley
- 1 small bunch of fresh oregano
- 5-6 leaves of fresh basil
- 5-6 leaves of fresh mint leaves
- 1 tbsp capers

- 4 anchovy fillets
- 2 tbsp red wine vinegar
- 6 tbsp olive oil
- 1 garlic clove
- Steamed cauliflower and broccoli to serve

Method

1 Pre-heat the oven to 400°F/200°C/Gas Mark 6 and grease a small baking dish.

2 Add the chicken thighs, garlic cloves, olive oil and lemon wedges and mix well to combine.

3 Roast in the oven for 45 minutes, until the chicken thighs are cooked through (check the juices run clear from the thickest part).

4 Place all of the salsa verde ingredients in to a food processor and blend until smooth (or leave a little chunky if you prefer).

5 When the chicken is cooked, divide between 2 plates, add the steamed vegetables and spoon over the salsa verde.

CHEF'S NOTE
This salsa verde is a source of protein and omega-3 from the anchovies. They add a lovely saltiness and can be used to enhance many savoury AIP dishes.

SPRING VEGETABLES AND HERB CHICKEN

AI
cookbook

Ingredients

- 4 chicken thighs
- 1 litre/1½ pints of chicken bone broth/stock
- 1 red onion, diced
- 2 garlic cloves, sliced
- 1 small bunch of flat leaf parsley
- 2 sprigs of lemon thyme

- 2 sprigs of marjoram
- 2 carrots, sliced thickly on the diagonal
- 1 celery stalk, sliced
- 1 lemon, zest only
- 150g/5oz asparagus spears, trimmed
- 150g/5oz broccoli florets, chopped
- ¼ savoy cabbage, shredded

Method

1 Put the chicken in a large lidded saucepan and add the chicken stock or bone broth. Add the onion, garlic, herbs, celery and carrots and bring to a boil.

2 Simmer with a lid on for 45 minutes, until the chicken is cooked and falling off the bones.

3 Add the lemon zest, asparagus, broccoli and cabbage to the pan and simmer for a further 5-6 minutes until softened.

4 Turn off the heat and leave to cool a little.

5 Remove the chicken and strip meat from the bones. Divide the meat between 2 bowls.

6 Pour over some of the broth and divide the vegetables between them.

CHEF'S NOTE

Use organic, pasture fed chicken for AIP recipes for the best nutrition. Avoiding protein that has been treated with unnecessary medication is essential to reduce toxins in our diets.

BRAISED TURKEY WITH GREMOLATA

SERVES 1

Ingredients

- 1 tbsp olive oil
- 1 small turkey escalope
- 1 small onion, diced
- 1 celery stick, sliced
- 1 small carrot, diced
- 300ml/10½floz vegetable stock
- 1 bay leaf

- 2 tbsp fresh thyme, chopped
- 100g/3½oz chestnut mushrooms, sliced

Gremolata
- 1 tbsp flat leaf parsley, chopped
- 1 tbsp lemon zest
- 1 garlic clove
- ½ tsp pink Himalayan sea salt

Method

1 Heat the olive oil in a saucepan and add the turkey escalope and brown all over. Add the onion, carrot, celery thyme, bay leaf, stock and mushrooms.

2 Bring to a boil and place on a lid.

3 Simmer for 8-10 minutes until the turkey is cooked through.

4 Place the turkey and vegetables on to a deep plate. Spoon over a bit of the stock.

5 Roughly chop all of the ingredients together for the gremolata until quite fine. Sprinkle over the turkey and serve immediately.

CHEF'S NOTE

Turkey is high in selenium, which is a great anti-oxidant and provides happy hormones for a good mood.

VENISON AND CRANBERRY HOT POT

AI
cookbook

Ingredients

- 1 tbsp olive oil
- 500g/1lb 2oz venison steak, cubed
- 1 onion, diced
- 1 garlic clove, crushed
- 2 carrots, diced
- 1 celery stalk, diced
- 1 tbsp fresh tarragon leaves, chopped
- 150g/5oz chestnut mushrooms, sliced
- 300ml vegetable stock
- ½ pink Himalayan sea salt
- 100g/3½oz fresh or frozen cranberries
- 1 tbsp gelatine + 4 tbsp hot water
- Steamed kale to serve

Method

1 Pre-heat the oven to 350°F/180°C/Gas Mark 4.

2 Heat the oil in a casserole dish and add the venison. Cook over a high heat until brown all over.

3 Add the onion, garlic, carrots and celery and stir over a medium heat for 5-6 minutes until softened.

4 Add the tarragon, mushrooms, stock, cranberries and salt and bring to a simmer.

5 Whisk the gelatine with the hot water and 1-2 minutes until frothy. Add to the casserole dish.

6 Place the casserole, covered, into the oven and cook for 1-1½ hours.

7 Serve with the steamed kale.

CHEF'S NOTE
Cranberries are antibacterial and commonly used to help prevent infections in the urinary tract, bladder and kidneys.

GRILLED MACKEREL, APPLES & SAUERKRAUT

Ingredients

- 2 small mackerel fillets, skin on
- 2 tsp olive oil
- 1 small bunch of parsley
- 1 garlic clove
- 1 celery stalk
- 1 tbsp lemon zest

- 1 tbsp lemon juice
- 1 tsp fresh ginger root, grated
- ¼ tsp pink Himalayan sea salt
- 2 tbsp sauerkraut
- 1 eating apple
- 1 tsp coconut aminos

Method

1 Place the mackerel fillets in a non-metallic bowl.

2 Add the celery, parsley, garlic, lemon zest, juice and salt in to a food processor and blend until smooth. Pour over the mackerel and leave to marinade for at least 2 hours.

3 When ready to cook, heat the grill to high and cook the mackerel on both sides for 3-4 minutes until crisp and cooked.

4 Core and slice the apple and mix with the sauerkraut.

5 Place onto a plate and top with the mackerel fillets.

CHEF'S NOTE

Mackerel is an easy to cook oily fish, full of omega-3. Aim to eat fish or shellfish 3 times a week when following an AIP eating plan.

LIVER, ONION AND "MASH"

AI
cookbook

Ingredients

- 1 tbsp olive oil
- 1 tbsp coconut flour
- 150g/5oz of lamb's liver
- 1 onion, halved and sliced
- 120ml/4floz bone broth/stock

- 1 tbsp flat leaf parsley, chopped
- 1 medium cauliflower head, cut in chunks
- 1 tbsp coconut milk
- 1 tsp gelatine
- ½ tsp pink Himalayan sea salt

Method

1 Heat the oil in a large frying pan.

2 Dust the liver with the flour and add to the pan. Fry over a high heat to brown all over for 3-4 minutes.

3 Add the onion slices and cook for a further 4-5 minutes to soften the onions.

4 Add the stock or bone broth and bring to a simmer.

5 Cook for a further 5 minutes and add the parsley.

6 Meanwhile, steam the cauliflower until soft.

7 Add to a blender and process. Whilst running add the gelatine and coconut milk (add extra to get the right consistency if necessary).

8 Add the salt and place onto a plate.

9 Top with the cooked liver, onion and pan juices.

CHEF'S NOTE
Try to include offal/organ meet to your diet once a week. Some cuts, like liver are really cheap and will add vital vitamin B12 to your diet.

GARLIC AND LEMON KEBABS

AI cookbook

Ingredients

- 2 tbsp coconut oil, melted
- 1 tbsp lemon zest
- 1 tsp raw honey
- 1 garlic clove, crushed
- 1 tbsp flat leaf parsley, chopped
- 1 courgette/zucchini, cut in to chunks

- 1 chicken breast or 1 pork fillet, chopped in mouth sized chunks
- 6 mushrooms, halved
- 1 handful of shredded iceberg
- ¼ cucumber, sliced

Method

1 Pre-heat the grill.

2 Mix the coconut oil, lemon zest, honey, garlic and parsley together.

3 Thread the pork or chicken on to skewers, alternating with the courgette/zucchini chunks and mushroom halves.

4 Brush the coconut oil mix on to the kebabs, all over. Place under a hot grill on a baking sheet and cook over a medium heat, brushing more oil on if necessary.

5 Turn over after 6-7 minutes and cook the same time again, to ensure the meat is cooked and the vegetables softened.

6 Place the shredded iceberg and cucumber on a plate and add the cooked kebabs.

CHEF'S NOTE

Make sure you always use raw honey when following an AIP eating plan, as this is unprocessed and unheated, still keeping all of the anti-microbial and immune boosting properties found in this natural sweetener.

LAMB AND CAULIFLOWER 'RICE'

AI
cookbook

Ingredients

- 2 garlic cloves
- 1 lemongrass stalk
- 1 thumb size piece fresh root ginger
- 1 tsp turmeric
- 1 tsp ground cinnamon
- 1 bunch fresh coriander

- 2 tbsp + 1 tsp olive oil
- 300g/11oz lamb fillet, cut into chunks
- 2 onions, sliced
- 1 courgette/zucchini, sliced diagonally
- 300ml/10½floz bone

- broth/meat stock
- 1 tbsp gelatine + 4 tbsp water)
- 1 tbsp coconut cream
- 200g/7oz spinach leaves
- 1 medium head of cauliflower
- 1 tbsp coconut oil, melted
- ½ tsp pink Himalayan sea salt

Method

1 Place the garlic, lemongrass, ginger, turmeric, cinnamon, most of the coriander and 2 tbsp olive oil in a blender. Process until smooth.

2 Heat the 1 tsp olive oil in a frying pan and add the lamb chunks. Cook over a high heat for 4-5 minutes to brown all over.

3 Add the garlic paste from the blender and stir well to coat the lamb. Cook for a further 3-4 minutes.

4 Add the onion and continue to cook for a further 4-5 minutes until soft. Add the courgette/zucchini slices and stock and bring to a simmer.

5 Mix the gelatine with the water and whisk for 1-2 minutes until frothy.

6 Pour in to the lamb mix and cook for a further 10 minutes to thicken and cook the lamb.

7 Stir in the coconut cream and spinach and remove from the heat (the spinach should wilt in the heat).

8 Process the cauliflower in a blender until it resembles rice.

9 Heat the coconut oil in a frying pan and add the cauliflower and salt. Heat for 4-5 minutes until the cauliflower is soft.

10 Divide the cauliflower between 2 plates and top with the lamb mix.

11 Scatter over the reaming chopped coriander/ cilantro to serve.

AUTOIMMUNE

· · · · · · · · · · · · · · · · · · ·

DESSERT

BAKED APPLES WITH CINNAMON CRUNCH

AI
cookbook

Ingredients

- 1 apple, cored
- ½ tsp ground cinnamon
- 1 tbsp coconut flour

- 2 tbsp coconut butter
- 1 tbsp maple syrup
- Coconut cream, whipped, to serve (see tip)

Method

1 Pre-heat the oven to 400°F/200°C/Gas Mark 6 and grease a small casserole dish.

2 Place the apple in the dish.

3 Mix the cinnamon, flour and butter together and create a lump texture.

4 Stuff some of this into the centre of the apple where the core was and sprinkle the rest over the apple.

5 Pour the maple syrup over the top and bake in the oven for 35-40 minutes until the apple is soft and oozing.

6 Serve with whipped coconut cream.

CHEF'S NOTE

Whipped coconut cream is a lovely treat on an AIP diet. If you leave a full fat tin of coconut milk in the fridge, you should be able to spoon off the separated thick top and whip it up with a whisk. Use the thinner milk to add to smoothies.

BANANA BREAD PUDDING WITH CACAO NIBS

AI
cookbook

Ingredients

- 1 tbsp gelatine + 4tbsp hot water
- 125g/4oz tigernut flour
- 75g/3oz tapioca starch
- 1 tsp ground cinnamon
- 4 tbsp coconut sugar
- 1 tsp baking powder

- 120ml/4floz coconut milk
- 2 bananas, peeled and mashed
- 3 tbsp cacao nibs
- Fresh fruit and coconut yoghurt to serve if desired

Method

1 Pre-heat the oven to 400°F/200°C/Gas Mark 6 and grease a small loaf tin.

2 Mix the gelatine with the water and whisk well for 1-2 minutes until frothy.

3 In a bowl, add the tigernut flour, tapioca, cinnamon, sugar, baking powder and cacao nibs.

4 Stir the bananas into the milk and add to the dry ingredients.

5 Beat in the gelatine mix and place in the loaf tin.

6 Level it off and bake in the oven for 30-35 minutes or until risen and cooked through.

7 Serve with fresh fruit and coconut yoghurt if desired.

CHEF'S NOTE

Tigernut flour is one of the only flours available on an AIP diet. It's made from a tuber, similar to yams and adds a lovely sweetness to bakes.

MANGO ICE WITH MINT CRUNCH

Ingredients

- 300g/11oz frozen mango chunks
- 120ml/4floz of coconut water
- 1 tbsp lime juice
- 1 tbsp lime zest
- 1 tsp raw honey
- 2 tbsp coconut sugar
- 7-8 fresh mint leaves

Method

1 On a board spread the mint leaves and coconut sugar, and chop. Mix until you have a coarse and sugary, minty blend.

2 Put the mango, coconut water, lime juice and zest and honey into a blender and process until smooth.

3 Scoop into two glasses and top with the mint sugar.

4 Serve immediately.

CHEF'S NOTE

Limes are considered low oxalate and can be helpful for those who are susceptible to developing kidney stones.

PEAR CRUNCH

Ingredients

- 3 pears, peeled, cored and sliced
- 1 tbsp maple syrup
- ½ tsp ground cinnamon
- ½ tsp ground ginger
- 4 tbsp coconut flour
- 1 tbsp coconut sugar
- 2 tbsp coconut flakes
- 1 tbsp coconut butter
- 2 tbsp coconut oil, melted

Method

1 Pre-heat the oven to 400°F/200°C/Gas Mark 6 and grease a small casserole dish.

2 Place the pears into the dish and mix well with the maple syrup and ground cinnamon.

3 In a bowl, add the coconut flour, sugar, ginger and coconut oil and flakes. Stir well and clump together to make a crumbly mix. Add a little water if this is still slightly dry.

4 Spoon the crumble mix on top of the pears.

5 Bake in the oven for 20-25 minutes, until the top is crunchy and the pears soft.

CHEF'S NOTE

This dessert uses a lot of coconut products – these are anti-inflammatory, metabolism boosting and hormone balancing and essential to make AIP easy and tasty.

BANANA AND BERRY ICE

AI
cookbook

Ingredients

- 2 bananas, peeled, chopped and frozen
- 200g/7oz frozen fruits of the forest (cherries, blackberries, etc.)
- 1 tbsp coconut milk

- 1 tbsp maple syrup
- 1 tbsp collagen powder
- 2 tbsp coconut flakes, toasted

Method

1 Place all of the ingredients except the collagen, into a blender and process until smooth.

2 Add the collagen and continue to process until light and whipped.

3 Divide between 2 glasses and serve with the toasted coconut flakes.

CHEF'S NOTE
Bananas are a great source of potassium, essential for heart muscle health and fluid balancing.

RASPBERRY SHORTCAKE

AI
cookbook

Ingredients

- 150g/5oz raspberries
- 1 tbsp maple syrup
- 125g/4oz cassava flour
- ¾ tsp baking powder

- 1 tbsp coconut sugar
- 40g/1½oz lard, fridge cold
- 4 tbsp coconut yoghurt

Method

1 Pre-heat the oven to 400°F/200°C/Gas Mark 6 and grease a baking tray.

2 Add the raspberries to a saucepan with the maple syrup. Heat gently to break down the berries. to make a raspberry syrup. Leave to cool.

3 Mix the flour, baking powder and sugar together and cut the lard into the dry ingredients with a knife.

4 When the flour and lard are like breadcrumbs, add enough cold water to make a firm dough.

5 Shape into 2 rounds and press down lightly onto the baking tray.

6 Bake for 15-20 minutes or until risen and coloured.

7 Allow to cool and then slice each shortcake in half.

8 Add two halves to a plate, top each with 1 tbsp of yoghurt and drizzle over the raspberry syrup.

CHEF'S NOTE
Raspberries are a great source of anthocyanidins, which act as powerful anti-oxidants.

AIP BROWNIE

Ingredients

- 1 tbsp gelatine + 5 tbsp hot water
- 120ml/4floz coconut oil
- 4 tbsp maple syrup
- 4 tbsp raw cacao powder

- 125g/4½oz tigernut flour
- 3 tbsp arrowroot starch
- 1 tsp baking powder

Method

1 Pre-heat the oven to 400°F/200°C/Gas Mark 6 and grease an 8"x8" baking tin.

2 Mix the gelatine with the hot water and whisk for 1-2 minutes, until frothy.

3 Add the maple syrup and coconut oil to the gelatine and mix well.

4 Put the cacao powder, tigernut flour, arrowroot and baking powder in a bowl and add the gelatine mix.

5 Beat well until combined.

6 Pour into the prepared tin and bake for 15-20 minutes until set on top but still lovely and squidgy underneath. You don't want to overcook this!

7 Cut in to 9 squares and serve warm or leave to cool.

CHEF'S NOTE

Use raw cacao powder here if you can. It provides better nutrition as the heating process removes the useful fatty acids, magnesium and iron it contains.

BLUEBERRY COBBLER

AI
cookbook

Ingredients

- 300g/11oz blueberries
- 2 tbsp coconut oil, melted
- 3 tbsp coconut milk
- 25g/1oz arrowroot starch

- 25g/1oz coconut flour
- 1 tsp baking powder
- 1 tsp ground cinnamon
- 2 tbsp raw honey

Method

1 Pre-heat the oven to 400°F/200°C/Gas Mark 6 and grease a square baking tray, roughly 8"x8".

2 Scatter the blueberries all over the bottom of the tray.

3 Mix all of the cobbler ingredients together well and beat to combine.

4 Place spoonful's of the mix over the top of the blueberries (don't worry too much if some of the blueberries still show through).

5 Place in the oven for 20-25 minutes until golden and risen. Serve warm.

CHEF'S NOTE
Blueberries are full of vitamin C and fibre and also contain high levels of flavonoids, which are thought to prevent cell damage.

73

GOOSEBERRY AND GINGER GALETTE

AI
cookbook

Ingredients

- 250g/9oz gooseberries
- 4 tbsp coconut sugar
- 1 tsp fresh ginger root, grated 75g/3oz tigernut flour
- 75g/3oz arrowroot flour
- 25g/1oz coconut flour

- ½ tsp ground ginger
- 4 tbsp coconut oil, melted
- 1 tbsp coconut sugar
- Enough coconut milk to combine

Method

1 Pre-heat the oven to 400°F/200°C/Gas Mark 6 and grease a baking tray.

2 Halve the gooseberries and mix with the grated ginger and coconut sugar for the filling. Leave to one side.

3 In a bowl, add the flours, ground ginger, coconut sugar and coconut oil. Mix with enough coconut milk to make a firm dough.

4 Press the dough on the baking tray and shape into a rough circle.

5 Place the gooseberries on top, leaving a 2cm margin and bring the pastry up around the edges to seal.

6 Bake for 25-30 minutes until the crust is cooked and the gooseberries soft and oozing.

CHEF'S NOTE
Gooseberries are rich in vitamin C and help the body to absorb iron and to aid the formation of collagen.

GRILLED BANANAS WITH PASSIONFRUIT DRIZZLE

AI
cookbook

Ingredients

- 2 large bananas
- 1 tsp ground cinnamon

- 2 passion fruit
- 1 tbsp maple syrup

Method

1 Pre-heat the grill.

2 Peel and slice the bananas in half, length ways,

3 Place onto a baking tray that fits under the grill.

4 Sprinkle on the cinnamon and grill for 3-4 minutes until toasted on top.

5 Halve the passion fruits and scoop out the flesh. Mix with the maple syrup.

6 Place 2 halves of the banana on a plate and drizzle over the passionfruit.

CHEF'S NOTE
Maple syrup is a good source of manganese, which is an essential mineral required for antioxidant defences. Use in moderation though as it's still a form of sweetener!

BLACKBERRIES AND CREAM PARFAIT

AI cookbook

Ingredients

- 150ml/5floz apple juice
- 2 tsp gelatine
- 200g/7oz coconut yoghurt

- 500g/1lb 2oz frozen blackberries/forest fruits
- 1 tsp maple syrup
- 1 tbsp toasted coconut flakes

Method

1 Heat the apple juice and bring to the boil. Whisk in the gelatine and stir until completely dissolved. Leave to cool.

2 Add the yoghurt and half of the fruit mix to a blender and process, pouring in the gelatine mix as it spins.

3 When combined, leave in the fridge to firm up.

4 Heat the remaining berries in the pan and add the syrup. Cook gently until they have broken down a little. Place in the fridge to cool.

5 When ready to serve, take 2 glasses and divide the yoghurt mix and fruit mix into layers.

6 Top with the coconut flakes.

CHEF'S NOTE
Blackberries are an excellent source of both soluble and insoluble fibre, great to promote good gut health.

MINT CHOC ICE

AI
cookbook

Ingredients

- 2 avocados
- 250ml/9floz coconut milk
- ½ tsp peppermint extract

- Handful of fresh mint leaves
- 2 tbsp maple syrup
- 1 tbsp raw cacao powder

Method

1 Peel and remove the stones from the avocados.

2 Place all of the ingredients into a blender. Process until smooth.

3 Pour into a plastic container suitable for the freezer.

4 Freeze for 2 hours and give a good stir.

5 Freeze for a further 2 hours.

6 Leave to sit in the fridge for ½ hour before serving.

CHEF'S NOTE
Avocados are a wonderful way to add creaminess to a dessert or bake and will give you a boost of hormone balancing, vitamin E.

GINGER AND APRICOT PUDDING

Ingredients

- 1 tbsp gelatine + 4 tbsp hot water
- 3 bananas, peeled and mashed
- 120ml/4floz of coconut oil, melted
- 120ml/4floz of raw honey
- 1 tsp ground ginger
- 60g/2½oz coconut flour
- 1 tsp baking powder
- 3 fresh apricots, destoned and sliced thinly
- Coconut yoghurt or cream to serve (optional)

Method

1 Pre-heat the oven to 375°F/190°C/Gas Mark 5 and grease a medium baking dish.

2 Mix the gelatine with the water and whisk until frothy.

3 Add all of the pudding ingredients together, apart from the apricots.

4 When well combined, add the apricots and gently stir in.

5 Pour into the baking dish and bake for 25-30 minutes until golden and risen.

6 Serve with coconut cream or yoghurt if desired.

CHEF'S NOTE
Apricots are rich in vitamin A and also associated with treating stomach issues, such as constipation.

APPLE AND CINNAMON PUDDING

AI
cookbook

Ingredients

- 3 apples, peeled, cored and diced
- 1 tbsp coconut oil
- 3 tbsp maple syrup
- 3 tsp ground cinnamon
- 250ml/8½floz coconut milk

- ½ avocado, peeled and stone removed
- 1 tbsp gelatine + 3 tbsp hot water
- Whipped coconut cream and apple slices to serve

Method

1 Place the apples, coconut oil and syrup into a saucepan and cook over a medium heat.

2 When the apples have broken down and soft, add the cinnamon.

3 Using a blender or stick blender, process the apples until really smooth.

4 Add the avocado and mix again until smooth and combined.

5 Whisk in the coconut milk.

6 Mix the gelatine with the water and whisk for 1-2 minutes until frothy.

7 Add the gelatine mix to the apple mix and pour equally into 2 glasses.

8 Store in the fridge for 2-3 hours to set.

9 Serve with a little whipped coconut cream and fresh apple slices on top.

CHEF'S NOTE

This mix could be used to fill an AIP pastry crust which has been pre-cooked. Store in the fridge and you have an apple tart!

FRUIT KEBAB WITH LEMON AND BASIL DRESSING

SERVES 2

Ingredients

- 4 slices of watermelon, cut into chunks
- 8 grapes
- 1 apple, cored and cut into chunks
- 8 small strawberries
- 1 banana, peeled and cut into chunks
- 4 tbsp lemon juice
- 1 tbsp raw honey
- 1 tbsp basil leaves, finely chopped

Method

1 Thread the fruit pieces onto skewers, alternating to separate the colours.

2 Mix the lemon juice, honey and basil leaves together to make a dressing.

3 Place the skewers onto 2 plates and drizzle over the dressing, ensuring all pieces of fruit are covered.

4 Serve immediately.

CHEF'S NOTE

Watermelon is a hydrating fruit to add to your diet. It contains Vitamin C and lycopene, both of which are useful for antioxidant protection and immune function boosting.

PUMPKIN PANNA COTTA WITH STEWED PEARS

Ingredients

- 1 tbsp gelatine + 3 tbsp hot water
- 400ml/14floz coconut milk
- 250ml/1 cup pumpkin puree
- 4 tbsp maple syrup
- 1 tsp ground cinnamon

- 2 pears, peeled, cored and sliced
- 1 tsp coconut oil
- 1 tbsp maple syrup
- 1 ground cinnamon

Method

1 Mix the gelatine with the hot water and whisk for 1-2 minutes until frothy.

2 Whisk the coconut milk, maple syrup and cinnamon together and add the gelatine mix.

3 Pour into 2 ramekins and place in the fridge for 3-4 hours until set.

4 Meanwhile place the pear pieces in a saucepan and add the oil, maple syrup and cinnamon. Cook over a medium heat until soft and cool in the fridge.

5 When ready to serve, place the ramekins on a plate and top with some of the stewed pear pieces.

CHEF'S NOTE

The essential oils found in cinnamon are considered to be helpful to treat a range of medical conditions, such as colds, asthma, insomnia, joint problems and digestive issues.

AUTOIMMUNE

. . . .

SNACKS

KIWI AND BANANA POWER SMOOTHIE

Ingredients

- 1 banana, peeled and chopped
- 2 kiwis, peeled and sliced
- 1 tbsp collagen powder
- 200ml/7floz coconut milk
- 1 tsp flaxseed oil

Method

1 Place all of the ingredients into a high-speed blender.

2 Process until smooth.

3 Serve chilled with crushed ice if you wish.

CHEF'S NOTE
Kiwis are a great source of vitamin C, potassium, magnesium, copper and phosphorous.

ELDERFLOWER AND GINGER SMOOTHIE

Ingredients

- ½ avocado, peeled and stone removed
- 250ml/8½floz coconut milk
- 1 elderflower head
- 1 apple, cored and cut into chunks
- 1 tsp fresh ginger root, grated

Method

1 Add the avocado, coconut milk, apple and ginger to a high-speed blender.

2 Pull the blossoms off the head of the elderflowers and add to the blender (do not add any stalks or leaves).

3 Process until all of the ingredients are smooth.

4 Serve immediately.

CHEF'S NOTE
When using elderflowers, be sure to only add the little blossoms to recipes as the stalks and leaves can produce some toxins.

CUCUMBER, SPINACH AND APPLE QUENCHER

AI
cookbook

Ingredients

- ½ avocado, peeled and stone removed
- 250ml/8½floz coconut water
- ¼ cucumber
- 1 apple, cored and cut into chunks
- 1 handful of baby spinach leaves

Method

1 Add the avocado and coconut to a high-speed blender.

2 Roughly chop the cucumber, keeping seeds and skin intact.

3 Add the apple and cucumber to the blender with the spinach.

4 Process until smooth.

CHEF'S NOTE
Coconut water is considered to be one of the best forms of hydration and makes a great base for a refreshing drink to boost electrolyte sodium levels.

PASSIONFRUIT AND MELON ENERGY DRINK

AI
cookbook

Ingredients

- 1 passionfruit, halved and seeds removed
- 150g/5oz melon, sliced
- 250ml/8½floz coconut water
- 50g/2oz fresh pineapple chunks
- 1 tbsp coconut oil, melted
- ½ tsp fresh ginger root, grated

Method

1 Add all of the ingredients into a high-speed blender.

2 Process until all of the ingredients are smooth and pour into a chilled glass.

3 Serve with plenty of ice.

CHEF'S NOTE
Coconut oil is considered to have great anti-flammatory and anti-oxidant properties and gives this drink a hit of energy.

CINNAMON HOT CHOCOLATE

Ingredients

- 400ml/14floz coconut milk
- 3 tbsp raw cacao powder
- 1 tbsp collagen powder

- ½ tsp ground cinnamon
- ½ tsp maple syrup

Method

1 Add all of the ingredients into a small saucepan.

2 Heat gently and bring to a boil.

3 Simmer for 4-5 minutes, whisking continually until thickened.

4 Pour into 2 heated mugs.

CHEF'S NOTE
Use collagen and not gelatine for drinks when adding this beneficial blend of amino-acids to drinks, as it won't form a gel and just thickens the drink.

COCONUT FAT BOMB SMOOTHIE

Ingredients

- 1 banana, peeled and chopped
- 250ml/8½floz coconut milk
- 1 tbsp coconut butter
- Handful of ice

Method

1 Place the banana, milk and butter into a high-speed blender and process until smooth.

2 Add the ice and whizz again.

3 Serve immediately.

CHEF'S NOTE

Coconut butter is a great ingredient to add to dishes when following an AIP diet. It's rich in healthy fats and contains fibre and nutrients and helpful as an anti-inflammatory aid too.

INDULGENT SPICED BROWNIE SMOOTHIE

AI
cookbook

Ingredients

- 1 piece of AIP brownie (from dessert section p72)
- 250ml/8½floz coconut milk
- ½ tsp ground cinnamon
- ½ banana, peeled and frozen
- ¼ tsp ground ginger

Method

1 Place all of the ingredients into a high-speed blender.

2 Process until everything is smooth.

3 Serve in a chilled glass as a treat.

CHEF'S NOTE
Using an AIP friendly brownie in this creates luxury in a glass.

BLUEBERRY, LIME AND MINT TONIC

AI
cookbook

Ingredients

- 150g/5oz blueberries
- 250ml/8½floz coconut water
- 1 tbsp lime juice

- 1 tsp raw honey
- 5-6 fresh mint leaves
- Large handful of ice

Method

1 Place all of the ingredients into a high-speed blender.

2 Process until the ingredients are smooth and the ice slushy.

3 Serve with lime wedges and extra mint leaves

CHEF'S NOTE

It is essential to stay hydrated regardless of what diet you follow. Creating tonics such as this will enable you to work towards reaching the recommended 8 glasses of fluid a day!

GINGER AND COCONUT BOUNCE BALLS

Ingredients

- 75g/3oz tigernut flour
- 25g/1oz coconut flour
- 1 tsp ground ginger
- 2 tbsp maple syrup

- 4 tbsp coconut oil, melted
- 1 tbsp collagen powder
- 2 tbsp desiccated coconut, to roll in

Method

1 Mix all of the ingredients together, apart from the desiccated coconut.

2 This should form a sticky dough, if not, add a little more maple syrup as this will depend on how absorbent your flours are.

3 Place the desiccated coconut on to a plate and roll the balls in it, to coat.

4 Place in the fridge to 'set' a little before serving.

CHEF'S NOTE
Coconut flour provides the body with lauric acid, which can help prevent infections and chronic diseases.

GUMMY SWEETS

Ingredients

- Juice of 1 lemon
- 200g/7oz frozen berries (any sort)
- 1 tbsp maple syrup
- 25g/1oz gelatine powder
- 100ml/3½floz water

Method

1 Add the berries and lemon juice to a blender and process until smooth.

2 Pour the mix into a saucepan and add the maple syrup, gelatine and water.

3 Bring to a boil and remove from the heat.

4 If necessary, blend again to make sure the mix is smooth.

5 Pour into a lined 8"x8" square baking tin and place in the fridge for at least an hour to set.

6 Remove from the fridge and turn out onto a board. Cut into 20 squares.

CHEF'S NOTE
Berries are packed with anti-inflammatory polyphenols, to help support the growth of good gut bacteria.

KALE CRISPS

AI
cookbook

Ingredients

- 400g/14oz kale
- 1 tbsp coconut oil, melted
- 1 tsp garlic powder

- 1 tsp onion powder
- ¼ tsp pink Himalayan sea salt

Method

1 Pre-heat the oven to 350°F/180°C/Gas Mark 4 and grease a large baking tray.

2 Wash and remove the thick stalks from the kale. Dry with kitchen towel.

3 Massage the kale with the coconut oil, garlic and onion powder and the salt until thoroughly coated.

4 Spread onto the baking tray and bake in the oven for 10-15 minutes, or until crisp.

CHEF'S NOTE
Kale is an excellent source of vitamin C, fibre, anti-oxidants and vitamin K, all useful when following an AIP eating plan.

HONEY COOKIES

Ingredients

- 2 tbsp avocado oil
- 2 tbsp raw honey
- 1 tbsp gelatine

- 50g/2oz coconut flour
- ¼ tsp baking powder

Method

1 Pre-heat the oven to 400°F/200°C/Gas Mark 6 and grease a large baking tray.

2 Mix the oil, honey and gelatine together and whisk until smooth.

3 Add the dry ingredients to the liquid and mix well.

4 Roll 9 balls from the dough (add a little water if your coconut flour is super absorbent!)

5 Flatten down on the baking tray and bake in the oven for 15-20 minutes.

6 When golden and cooked, cool on a rack.

CHEF'S NOTE
You could add some cacao nibs or dried fruit (in moderation) to the mix for variety.

COURGETTE/ZUCCHINI CHIPS

AI
cookbook

Ingredients

- 2 large courgettes/zucchini, cut into matchsticks
- 1 tbsp coconut oil, melted
- 1 tbsp coconut flour
- ½ tsp pink Himalayan sea salt
- 1 tbsp onion powder
- 1 tbsp dried oregano

Method

1 Pre-heat the oven to 400°F/200°C/Gas Mark 6 and grease a baking tray.

2 Mix the courgette/zucchini matchsticks with the oil, coconut flour, salt, onion powder and oregano.

3 Tip onto the baking tray and bake for 20-25 minutes until crisp.

4 Serve immediately.

CHEF'S NOTE
Courgettes/zucchini are full of vitamins C and K. This snack would make a great side dish for a main course.